ROVING ROSIE REPORTS

BY

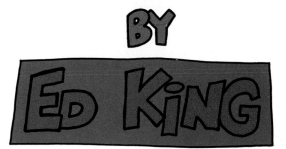

ED KING

I'M GUS.
LOOK FOR ME
IN THIS BOOK.
(I've got my own book too!)

I'M WILLIAM.
LOOK FOR ME
IN THIS BOOK.
(I've got my own book too!)

I'M LUCY.
LOOK FOR ME
IN THIS BOOK.
(I've got my own book too!)

CHECKERBOARD PRESS ✦ **NEW YORK**

Copyright © 1991 Checkerboard Press, Inc. All rights reserved.
ISBN: 1-56288-010-1 Library of Congress Catalog Card Number: 90-27867
Printed in U.S.A. 0 9 8 7 6 5 4 3 2 1

It's Rosie the Reporter's first day on the job, and the bank is being robbed. Rosie is at the scene to get the whole story. Can you find Rosie and:

- Acrobats
- Alligator
- Arab
- Artist
- Baby's bottle
- 4 Bank robbers
- Binoculars
- 7 Briefcases
- Broom
- 4 Cats
- Chair
- Cliff edge
- Cowboy
- 10 Dogs
- Dustpan
- Earphones
- Easel
- Electric cord
- Fire hydrant
- Getaway car
- Hiker
- Jogging wolf
- Jump rope
- Monkey
- Musical notes
- Paint cans

- Photographer
- Pied Piper
- Pole vaulter
- Police officers
- Popcorn seller
- Quintuplets
- Rabbit
- Raccoon
- 12 Rats
- Roller skates
- 10 Runners
- Scooter
- Sculpture
- 2 Skateboards
- Skunk
- Spy
- Stroller
- Telephone booth
- Tightrope walker
- Turtle
- 2 Weight lifters
- Yogi
- ...and lots more!

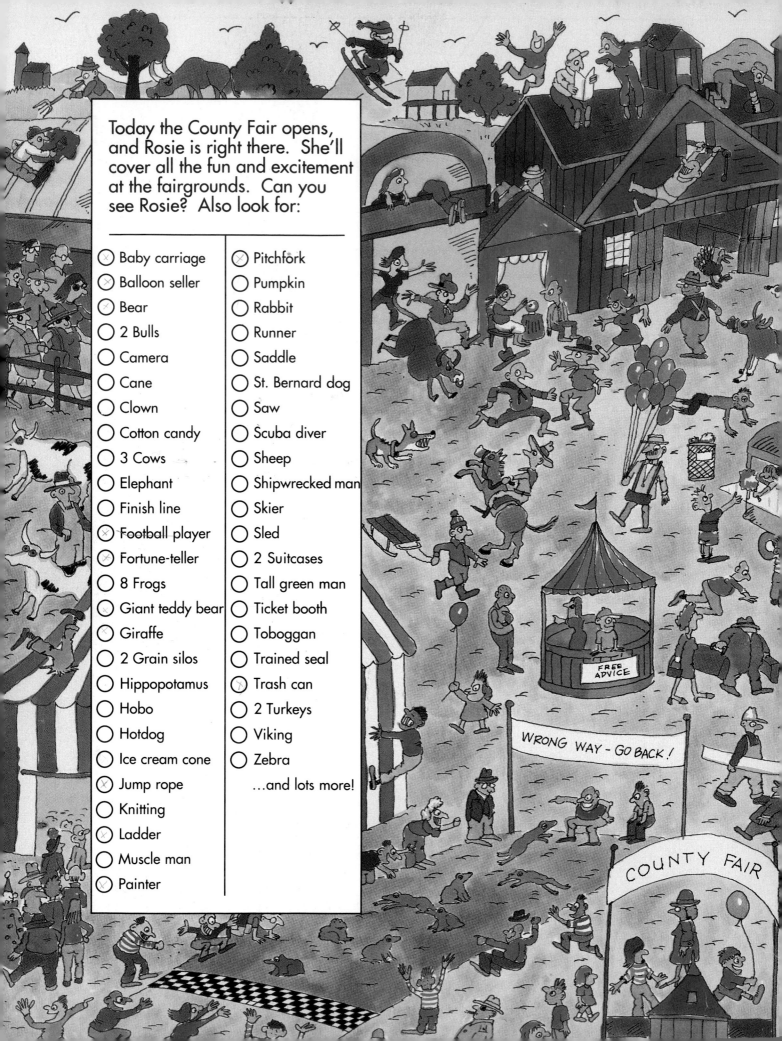

Today the County Fair opens, and Rosie is right there. She'll cover all the fun and excitement at the fairgrounds. Can you see Rosie? Also look for:

- ⊗ Baby carriage
- ⊗ Balloon seller
- ⊗ Bear
- ◯ 2 Bulls
- ◯ Camera
- ◯ Cane
- ◯ Clown
- ◯ Cotton candy
- ◯ 3 Cows
- ◯ Elephant
- ◯ Finish line
- ⊗ Football player
- ⊗ Fortune-teller
- ◯ 8 Frogs
- ◯ Giant teddy bear
- ◯ Giraffe
- ◯ 2 Grain silos
- ◯ Hippopotamus
- ◯ Hobo
- ◯ Hotdog
- ◯ Ice cream cone
- ⊗ Jump rope
- ◯ Knitting
- ⊗ Ladder
- ◯ Muscle man
- ◯ Painter

- ⊗ Pitchfork
- ◯ Pumpkin
- ◯ Rabbit
- ◯ Runner
- ◯ Saddle
- ◯ St. Bernard dog
- ◯ Saw
- ◯ Scuba diver
- ◯ Sheep
- ◯ Shipwrecked man
- ◯ Skier
- ◯ Sled
- ◯ 2 Suitcases
- ◯ Tall green man
- ◯ Ticket booth
- ◯ Toboggan
- ◯ Trained seal
- ⊗ Trash can
- ◯ 2 Turkeys
- ◯ Viking
- ◯ Zebra
  ...and lots more!

FREE ADVICE

WRONG WAY - GO BACK !

COUNTY FAIR

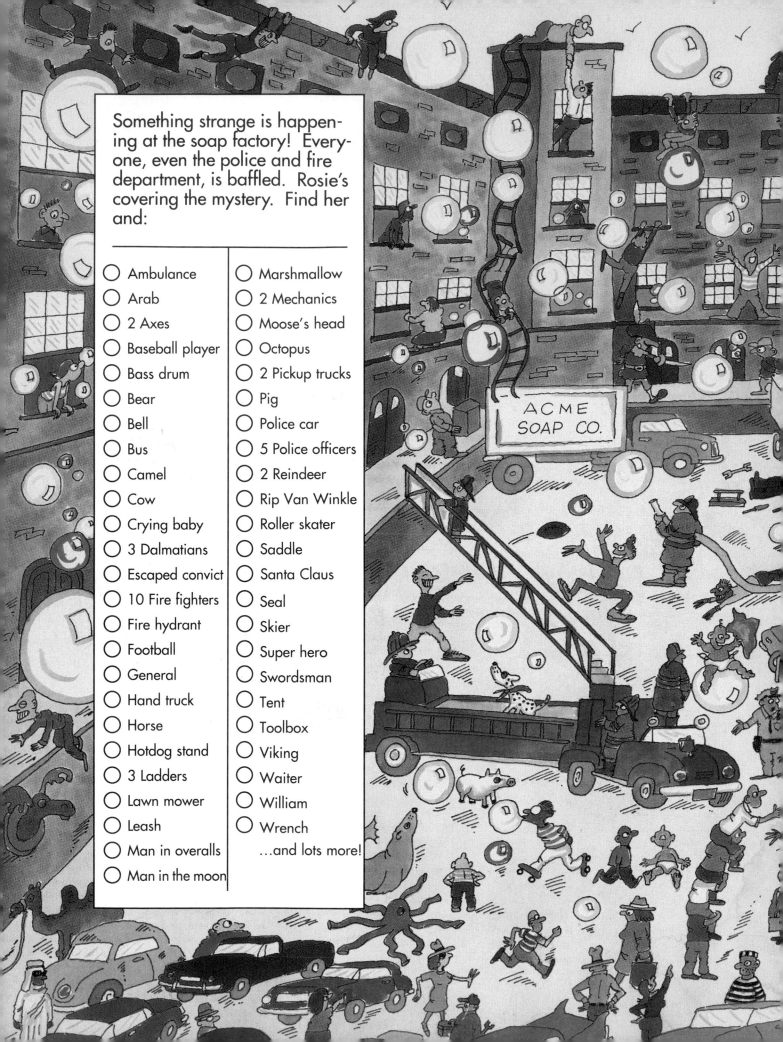

Something strange is happening at the soap factory! Everyone, even the police and fire department, is baffled. Rosie's covering the mystery. Find her and:

- Ambulance
- Arab
- 2 Axes
- Baseball player
- Bass drum
- Bear
- Bell
- Bus
- Camel
- Cow
- Crying baby
- 3 Dalmatians
- Escaped convict
- 10 Fire fighters
- Fire hydrant
- Football
- General
- Hand truck
- Horse
- Hotdog stand
- 3 Ladders
- Lawn mower
- Leash
- Man in overalls
- Man in the moon
- Marshmallow
- 2 Mechanics
- Moose's head
- Octopus
- 2 Pickup trucks
- Pig
- Police car
- 5 Police officers
- 2 Reindeer
- Rip Van Winkle
- Roller skater
- Saddle
- Santa Claus
- Seal
- Skier
- Super hero
- Swordsman
- Tent
- Toolbox
- Viking
- Waiter
- William
- Wrench
  ...and lots more!

ACME SOAP CO.

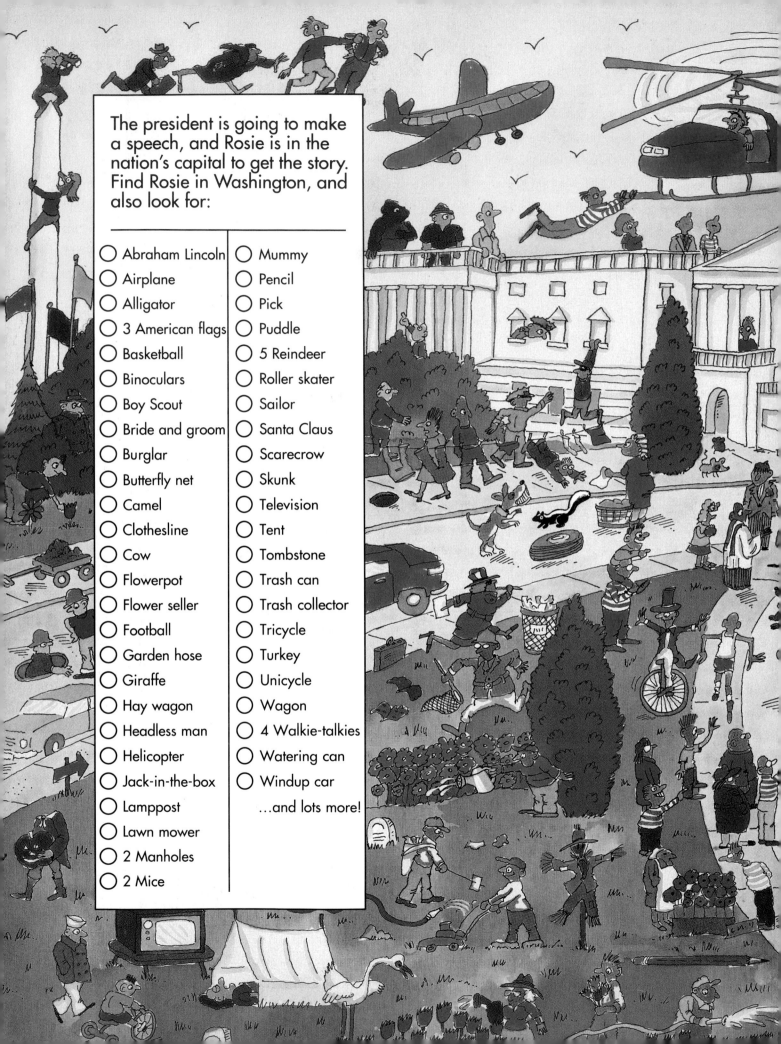

The president is going to make a speech, and Rosie is in the nation's capital to get the story. Find Rosie in Washington, and also look for:

- Abraham Lincoln
- Airplane
- Alligator
- 3 American flags
- Basketball
- Binoculars
- Boy Scout
- Bride and groom
- Burglar
- Butterfly net
- Camel
- Clothesline
- Cow
- Flowerpot
- Flower seller
- Football
- Garden hose
- Giraffe
- Hay wagon
- Headless man
- Helicopter
- Jack-in-the-box
- Lamppost
- Lawn mower
- 2 Manholes
- 2 Mice

- Mummy
- Pencil
- Pick
- Puddle
- 5 Reindeer
- Roller skater
- Sailor
- Santa Claus
- Scarecrow
- Skunk
- Television
- Tent
- Tombstone
- Trash can
- Trash collector
- Tricycle
- Turkey
- Unicycle
- Wagon
- 4 Walkie-talkies
- Watering can
- Windup car
- ...and lots more!

History is being made at Cape Canaveral. A multiple rocket launch is underway. Rosie is there reporting the news. See if you can find her and:

- Army tank
- Artist
- 6 Astronauts
- Ball
- 3 Balloons
- Barbecue grill
- Bear
- Biplane
- Bird
- Blimp
- Boot
- Bricklayer
- Broom
- Bucket
- Cactus
- Cardboard box
- Caveman
- Cow
- Goat
- Guitar player
- Guru
- Hot air balloon
- Hula-Hoop
- Ice cream cart
- Logs
- Mail carrier
- Mountain climbers
- Oil well
- Palm tree
- Paper airplane
- Paperboy
- Philosopher
- Pitchfork
- 3 Police officers
- Reindeer
- Robot
- Rocking chair
- Sailor
- Screwdriver
- Scuba diver
- Sheep
- Snow shovel
- Sunbathers
- Telescope
- Television camera
- Turkey
- Umbrella
- Wagon
- Wheelbarrow
  ...and lots more!

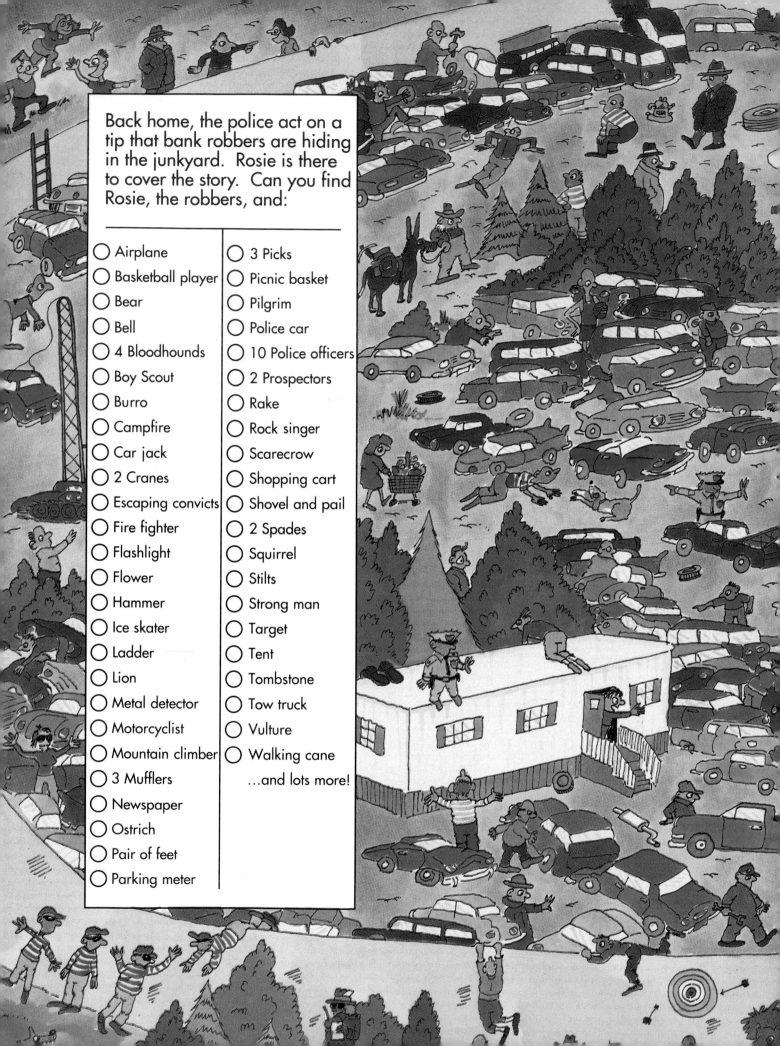

Back home, the police act on a tip that bank robbers are hiding in the junkyard. Rosie is there to cover the story. Can you find Rosie, the robbers, and:

- ◯ Airplane
- ◯ Basketball player
- ◯ Bear
- ◯ Bell
- ◯ 4 Bloodhounds
- ◯ Boy Scout
- ◯ Burro
- ◯ Campfire
- ◯ Car jack
- ◯ 2 Cranes
- ◯ Escaping convicts
- ◯ Fire fighter
- ◯ Flashlight
- ◯ Flower
- ◯ Hammer
- ◯ Ice skater
- ◯ Ladder
- ◯ Lion
- ◯ Metal detector
- ◯ Motorcyclist
- ◯ Mountain climber
- ◯ 3 Mufflers
- ◯ Newspaper
- ◯ Ostrich
- ◯ Pair of feet
- ◯ Parking meter
- ◯ 3 Picks
- ◯ Picnic basket
- ◯ Pilgrim
- ◯ Police car
- ◯ 10 Police officers
- ◯ 2 Prospectors
- ◯ Rake
- ◯ Rock singer
- ◯ Scarecrow
- ◯ Shopping cart
- ◯ Shovel and pail
- ◯ 2 Spades
- ◯ Squirrel
- ◯ Stilts
- ◯ Strong man
- ◯ Target
- ◯ Tent
- ◯ Tombstone
- ◯ Tow truck
- ◯ Vulture
- ◯ Walking cane

...and lots more!

MORGAN HIGHWAY
AUTO SALVAGE

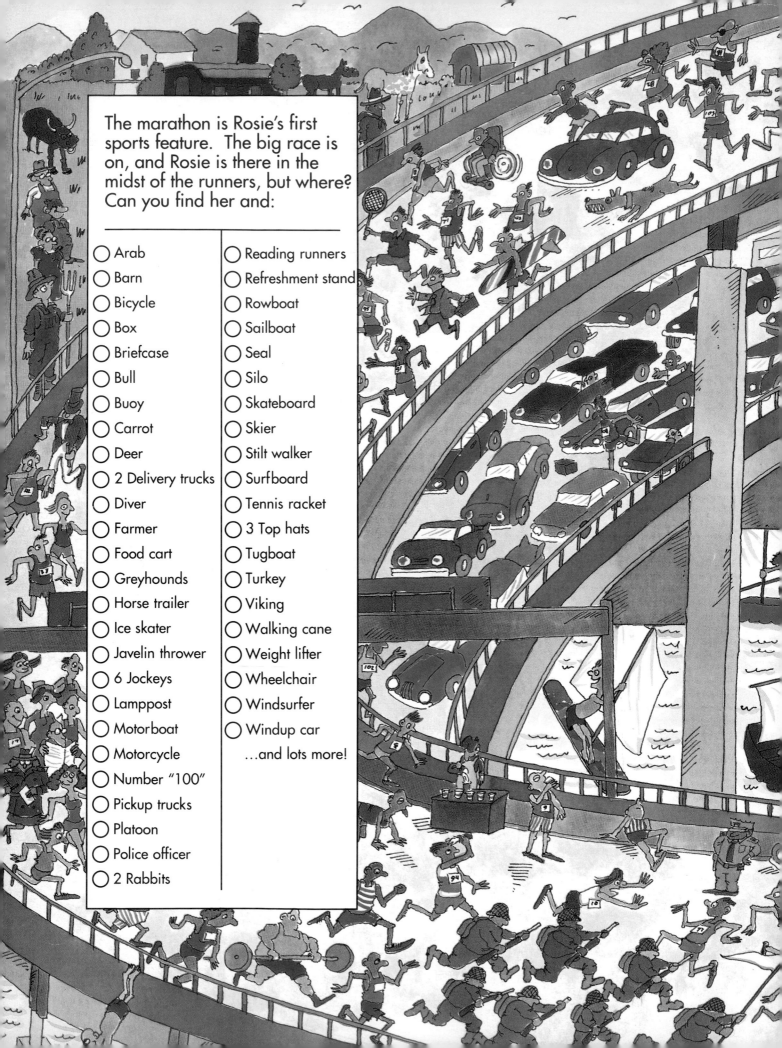

The marathon is Rosie's first sports feature. The big race is on, and Rosie is there in the midst of the runners, but where? Can you find her and:

- ○ Arab
- ○ Barn
- ○ Bicycle
- ○ Box
- ○ Briefcase
- ○ Bull
- ○ Buoy
- ○ Carrot
- ○ Deer
- ○ 2 Delivery trucks
- ○ Diver
- ○ Farmer
- ○ Food cart
- ○ Greyhounds
- ○ Horse trailer
- ○ Ice skater
- ○ Javelin thrower
- ○ 6 Jockeys
- ○ Lamppost
- ○ Motorboat
- ○ Motorcycle
- ○ Number "100"
- ○ Pickup trucks
- ○ Platoon
- ○ Police officer
- ○ 2 Rabbits

- ○ Reading runners
- ○ Refreshment stand
- ○ Rowboat
- ○ Sailboat
- ○ Seal
- ○ Silo
- ○ Skateboard
- ○ Skier
- ○ Stilt walker
- ○ Surfboard
- ○ Tennis racket
- ○ 3 Top hats
- ○ Tugboat
- ○ Turkey
- ○ Viking
- ○ Walking cane
- ○ Weight lifter
- ○ Wheelchair
- ○ Windsurfer
- ○ Windup car
  ...and lots more!

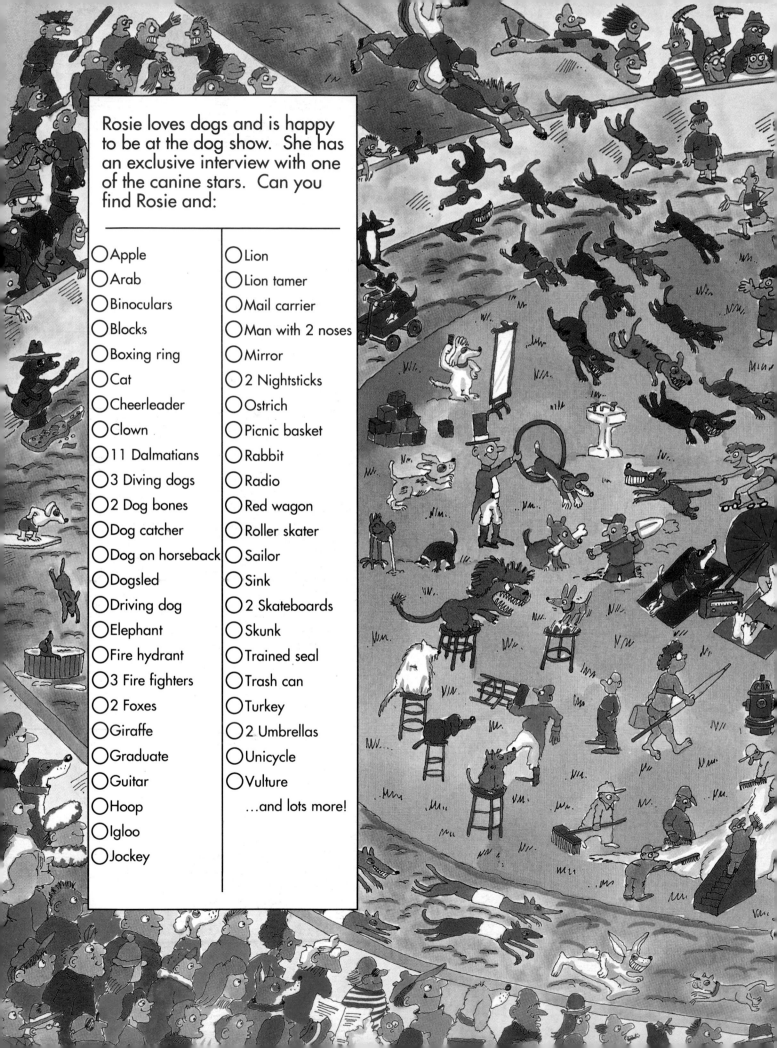

Rosie loves dogs and is happy to be at the dog show. She has an exclusive interview with one of the canine stars. Can you find Rosie and:

- Apple
- Arab
- Binoculars
- Blocks
- Boxing ring
- Cat
- Cheerleader
- Clown
- 11 Dalmatians
- 3 Diving dogs
- 2 Dog bones
- Dog catcher
- Dog on horseback
- Dogsled
- Driving dog
- Elephant
- Fire hydrant
- 3 Fire fighters
- 2 Foxes
- Giraffe
- Graduate
- Guitar
- Hoop
- Igloo
- Jockey
- Lion
- Lion tamer
- Mail carrier
- Man with 2 noses
- Mirror
- 2 Nightsticks
- Ostrich
- Picnic basket
- Rabbit
- Radio
- Red wagon
- Roller skater
- Sailor
- Sink
- 2 Skateboards
- Skunk
- Trained seal
- Trash can
- Turkey
- 2 Umbrellas
- Unicycle
- Vulture
  ...and lots more!

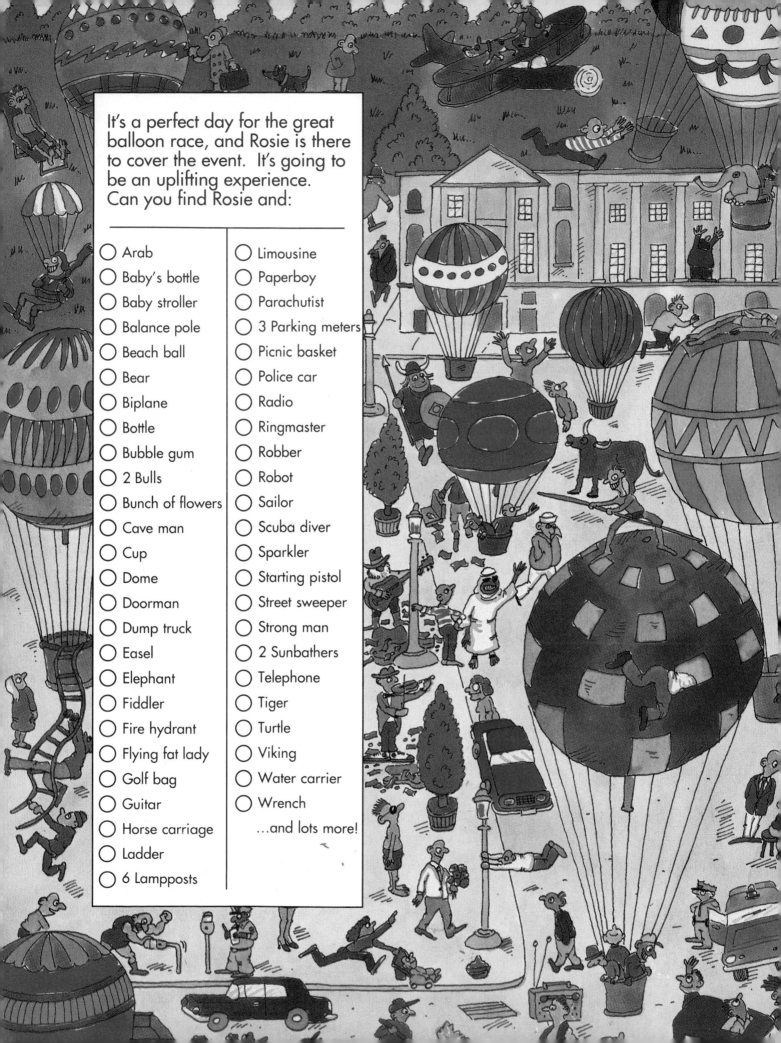

It's a perfect day for the great balloon race, and Rosie is there to cover the event. It's going to be an uplifting experience. Can you find Rosie and:

- Arab
- Baby's bottle
- Baby stroller
- Balance pole
- Beach ball
- Bear
- Biplane
- Bottle
- Bubble gum
- 2 Bulls
- Bunch of flowers
- Cave man
- Cup
- Dome
- Doorman
- Dump truck
- Easel
- Elephant
- Fiddler
- Fire hydrant
- Flying fat lady
- Golf bag
- Guitar
- Horse carriage
- Ladder
- 6 Lampposts

- Limousine
- Paperboy
- Parachutist
- 3 Parking meters
- Picnic basket
- Police car
- Radio
- Ringmaster
- Robber
- Robot
- Sailor
- Scuba diver
- Sparkler
- Starting pistol
- Street sweeper
- Strong man
- 2 Sunbathers
- Telephone
- Tiger
- Turtle
- Viking
- Water carrier
- Wrench
- ...and lots more!

A freak snowstorm catches the city by surprise, and Rosie is up to her knees in the white stuff. The kids love it, and so does Rosie. See if you can find her and:

- ○ Apple
- ○ Bikini
- ○ Bowling ball
- ○ Boxer
- ○ Cactus
- ○ Campfire
- ○ Cellar
- ○ Chair
- ○ Chimney
- ○ Cow skull
- ○ Father Time
- ○ Frying pan
- ○ Goose
- ○ Hockey puck
- ○ 4 Ice climbers
- ○ Ice skating rink
- ○ Igloo
- ○ Jack-o'-lantern
- ○ Mail carrier
- ○ Palm tree
- ○ Paperboy
- ○ Penguin
- ○ Piano
- ○ Picket fence
- ○ Polar bear

- ○ 2 Police officers
- ○ Radio
- ○ Reindeer
- ○ Ruler
- ○ St. Bernard dog
- ○ Sasquatch
- ○ Skis
- ○ Sled
- ○ Sleigh
- ○ 2 Snowmobiles
- ○ Snowplow
- ○ Snowshoes
- ○ Square snowman
- ○ Statue
- ○ Stop sign
- ○ Stilts
- ○ Sunlamp
- ○ Surfboard
- ○ Swing
- ○ Syrup tap
- ○ Tent
- ○ 3 Toboggans
- ○ Tow truck
- ○ Umbrella
- ...and lots more!

Rosie is in Hollywood for a great movie opening. The stars are out and Rosie is there to report it. Can you find Rosie and:

○ Airplane
○ Baby's bottle
○ Bag of donuts
○ Balloons
○ Beach ball
○ Bench
○ Billboard
○ 2 Binoculars
○ Blimp
○ 4 Boy Scouts
○ Briefcase
○ Burglar
○ Cat
○ Cheerleader
○ Chef's hat
○ Doorman
○ Ducklings
○ Fire hydrant
○ Fur stole
○ Giant donut
○ Golf bag
○ Gorilla
○ Horse
○ Horseshoe
○ Hotdog stand
○ 2 Monsters

○ Moose
○ Motorcycle
○ 2 Mountaineers
○ Mouse
○ Movie stars
○ 9 Palm trees
○ Pilgrim
○ 3 Police officers
○ Poodle
○ Sign painter
○ 2 Skateboards
○ Sleeping bag
○ Spaceman
○ 3 Spotlights
○ Ticket window
○ Tightrope walker
○ Tin cans
○ Top
○ Trash can
○ Turtle
○ Window washer
   ...and lots more!

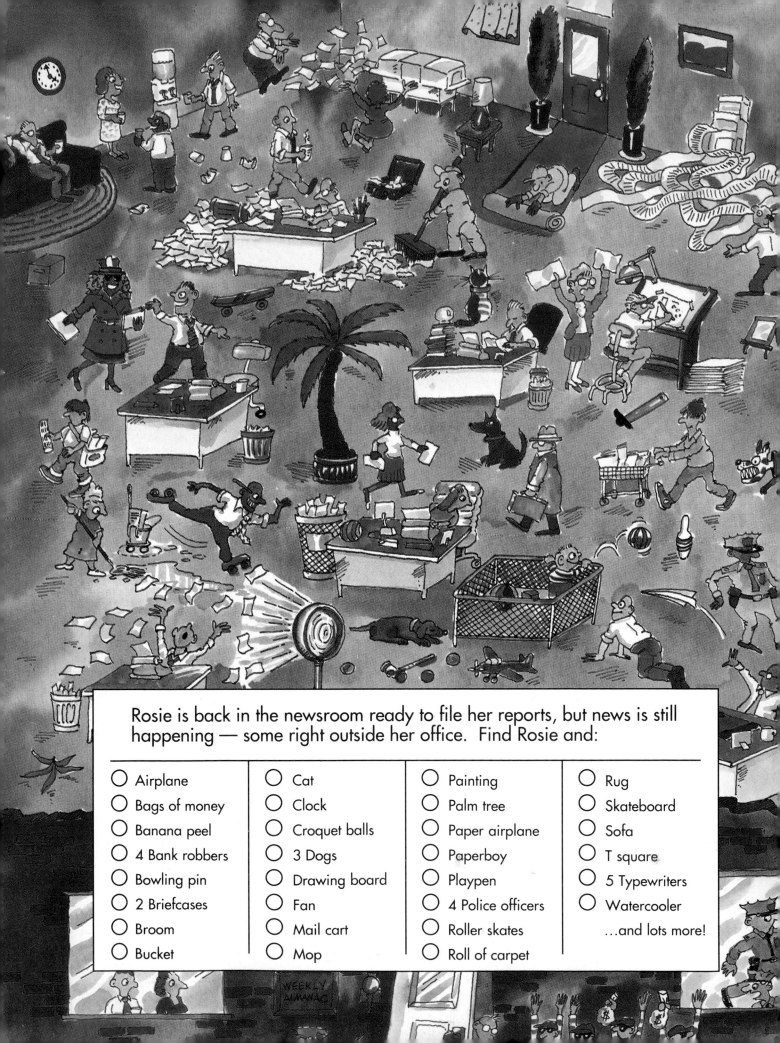

Rosie is back in the newsroom ready to file her reports, but news is still happening — some right outside her office. Find Rosie and:

- ○ Airplane
- ○ Bags of money
- ○ Banana peel
- ○ 4 Bank robbers
- ○ Bowling pin
- ○ 2 Briefcases
- ○ Broom
- ○ Bucket

- ○ Cat
- ○ Clock
- ○ Croquet balls
- ○ 3 Dogs
- ○ Drawing board
- ○ Fan
- ○ Mail cart
- ○ Mop

- ○ Painting
- ○ Palm tree
- ○ Paper airplane
- ○ Paperboy
- ○ Playpen
- ○ 4 Police officers
- ○ Roller skates
- ○ Roll of carpet

- ○ Rug
- ○ Skateboard
- ○ Sofa
- ○ T square
- ○ 5 Typewriters
- ○ Watercooler
- …and lots more!